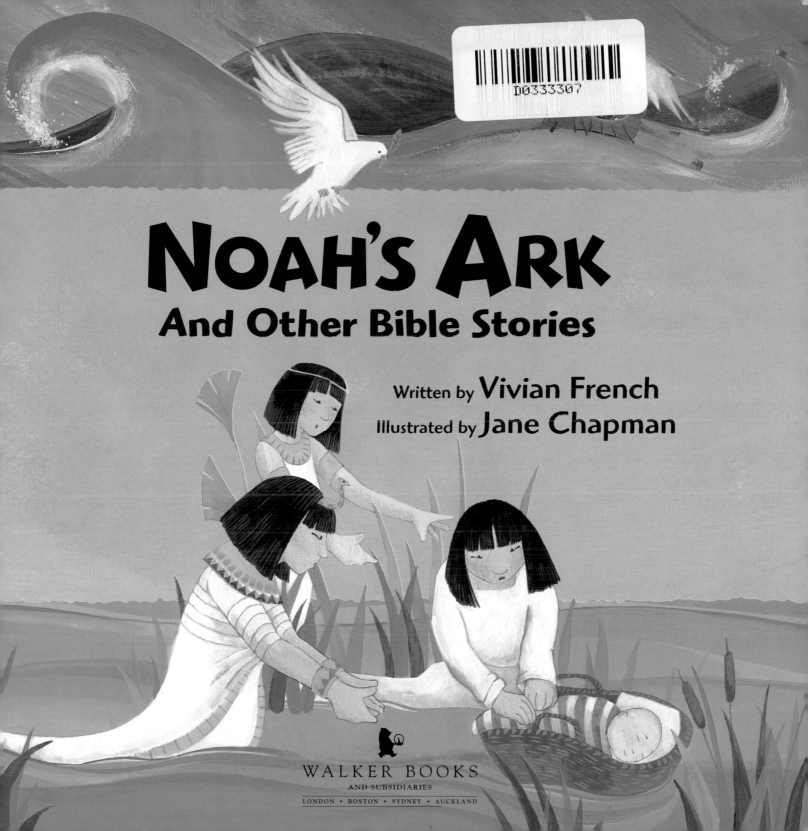

NOAH'S ARK
And Other Bible Stories

Written by **Vivian French**

Illustrated by **Jane Chapman**

WALKER BOOKS
AND SUBSIDIARIES

LONDON · BOSTON · SYDNEY · AUCKLAND

NOAH'S ARK

In the beginning God made the world. He made land, and he made sea, and he made animals and he made people.

The people that God made did not look after each other or their beautiful new world. God told them he was angry, but they took no notice. They just went on being bad.

God was very sad. He went to find Noah, who was a good man, and a special friend of God's. God told Noah that he must build an ark and he must make it out of the yellow wood of the gopher tree and cover it with sticky black tar so that it did not let in water.

"I am going to cover the world with water," God said. "All the bad people will be washed away, but I will look after you and your family. You must collect the animals, and the birds, and the little things that creep and crawl, and bring two of every kind into the ark. Take enough food for everybody. I will look after you all. I am going to make it rain for forty days and forty nights, and nothing will be left on earth."

Noah and his family set to work and built the ark exactly as God had told them. They found two of every kind of animal and two of every sort of bird, and two of all the creepy crawly things ... and they led them all into the ark, two by two.

Then Noah and his wife went after them, and his three sons and their wives went in too ... and God shut the door.

Then God made it rain. It rained and it rained and it rained, and the earth was covered in deep deep water.

The ark floated away, and only Noah, his family and the animals in the ark were left alive.

The water was over the earth for many months, but God had not forgotten Noah. He sent a wind, and as the wind began to blow the rain stopped and the water began to go down.

At last, a long time after the rains began, the ark touched the earth again. It rested on the top of a mountain, and when Noah peered through the window he could see the tips of the tops of mountains showing above the water.

Noah waited forty more days, and then he opened the window. He sent a dove flying out to see if the water had all gone, but the dove soon came back.

There was nowhere for her to perch, and Noah put his hand out and took her back into the ark.

Seven days later Noah sent the dove out again, and this time she came flying back with an olive leaf in her beak. Noah was very pleased because he knew that now the trees and the plants were growing.

Seven days later Noah sent the dove out again. This time she did not come back at all, and Noah and his family and all the animals cheered and cheered – the water must have gone.

Noah opened up the ark, and looked out. The earth was fresh and sweet, and quite safe.

"You can leave the ark now," God said. "Take your family, and all the animals and the birds and the little creepy crawly things, and go out into my beautiful world."

The animals hopped and skipped out of the ark, the birds flapped and flew, and the little things crept and crawled as fast as they could go. Noah and his family hurried out as well, but they did not forget how God had looked after them. They had a celebration to say thank you, and God was very pleased.

"I will always look after you," God told Noah. "You and your children and your children's children too ... and I will make you a promise. I promise that I will never ever destroy the earth again ... and I will give you a sign to remind both me and you of this promise."

God smiled at Noah, and he spread his arms out wide.

"You will see my sign every time it rains when the sun is in the sky. Every time there is sun and rain together, look up and you will see it...

You will see my rainbow."

MOSES IN THE BULRUSHES

Long ago there was a man called Joseph. Joseph was
a special friend of God, and God looked after him.
  Joseph had a great many brothers and sisters.
When Joseph's father was old, they all moved to a
place called Egypt. The people in Egypt were pleased
to have Joseph and his sons and daughters and
nephews and nieces in their country.

"We are Egyptians, and you are Hebrews, but we can live together," they said.

The years went by, however, and Joseph's family grew bigger and bigger. When Joseph was a hundred and ten years old he died, but his family went on growing. The sons and daughters and nephews and nieces all had families of their own. Then their families had families too.

A new king ruled over Egypt. He saw how many people were related to Joseph, and he was worried.

"There are more Hebrew men and women and children than there are Egyptians!" he said. "What if they decide to fight against us? The Egyptians would never win!"

The king decided to make new laws. He ordered all Joseph's relations to work very hard indeed. They were not paid any money, and they were treated very badly. Even so, they went on marrying and having more and more babies.

The king became angry. "Why are there so many of these people?" he demanded. "We must do something else! Don't hurt the girl babies – but throw all the boy babies in the river!"

One Hebrew mother had just had a baby boy. She heard what the king said and she was very frightened. She hid her baby so that the Egyptian soldiers could not find him and hurt him.

When the baby was three months old he was almost too big to hide. His mother had an idea. She made him a basket out of bulrushes, and painted it with sticky black tar so that it was watertight. Then, very carefully, she tucked the baby inside. She hid the basket in the long grass at the edge of the river, and waited. The baby's big sister stood close by.

It wasn't long before the king's daughter came down to the river to bathe. Her servants walked along the river bank, but the princess stepped into the cool clear water – and saw the basket.

"What's that?" she asked. "Please bring it here!"

One of the servant girls went to fetch the basket. The princess opened it, and she found the baby. She picked him up and cuddled him.

"This must be a Hebrew baby," she said quietly.

The baby's sister had been watching. She came hurrying along the river bank and curtsied to the princess.

"Shall I find a woman who could look after the baby for you?" she asked.

The princess nodded. "Yes," she said. "Please do."

At once the baby's sister ran to fetch her mother. The princess gave her the baby, and asked her to look after him. "I'll pay you well," the princess said.

The baby's mother looked after the baby until he was one year old, and then she took him to the royal palace.

"He will be my son now," the princess said. "I will call him Moses, because that name means 'out of the water'."

And Moses' mother and sister smiled at each other, because they knew that now Moses would always be safe.

JONAH AND THE BIG FISH

Once there was a city called Ninevah. The men and women and children who lived there told lies and cheated and hurt each other. God watched them for a while, and then he called for a man named Jonah.

"Jonah," God said, "I have something very important for you to do. You must go to Ninevah, and tell the people I know what terrible things they have done. Tell them they must stop being so bad."

Jonah heard what God said, but he didn't want to go to Ninevah. The people there were his enemies, and he didn't want to help them. He ran away instead. He ran all the way to a town called Joppa, and jumped on to a ship that was sailing to Spain.

"God won't find me here," Jonah said to himself, and he went down into the bottom of the boat to sleep.

But God knew exactly where Jonah was. He sent one of his strongest winds, and it blew the sea into a terrible storm. The sailors were very frightened.

"The ship is sinking!" they shouted. "Help! Help!"

Jonah did not hear them. He was fast asleep.

The wind went on blowing, and the waves grew higher and higher.

"Quick! Throw the cargo overboard!" the sailors yelled. "All the barrels and boxes and baskets! Maybe that will save the ship!"

Jonah went on sleeping. He didn't wake up until the captain shook him.

"How can you sleep at a time like this?" the captain asked. "Quick! Pray for help – maybe God will hear you and save us!"

The sailors were getting more and more worried. "God must be angry with one of us!" they said. "Who can it be?"

They took a bunch of straws, and they each pulled one out. Jonah's straw was the shortest.

"It must be you!" said the sailors. "Who are you? What have you done?"

Jonah knew he had to tell the truth. "God told me to go to Ninevah," he said, "but I didn't go. I ran away instead."

The sailors stared at Jonah as the storm raged about them.

"No wonder God is angry!" they said. "But what can we do?"

"You must throw me into the waves," Jonah told them, "and then the storm will go away."

At first the sailors wouldn't do as Jonah said. They tried as hard as they could to row the ship to land. It was no good. The wind blew stronger, and the waves grew higher. At last the sailors gave up. "Please forgive us, God!" they called out. "We don't want to hurt Jonah, but you sent the storm!" And they threw Jonah over the side of the ship.

As soon as he splashed into the water the wind stopped blowing.

Jonah sank down and down to the bottom of the sea ... but God was still watching. He sent a huge fish, and the fish swallowed Jonah in one big gulp.

Glug, glug, glug ... Jonah slid into the fish's belly. It was very dark, but Jonah was safe. He sat in the darkness for three days and three nights, and he did a lot of thinking.

"God," he said at last, "I am very sorry. You saved me from drowning at the bottom of the sea. I will do what you asked me to do."

When God heard Jonah he told the fish to let him go. The fish swam up to a beach and opened its mouth wide – and Jonah walked out.

"Now, Jonah," God said. "Go to Ninevah, and give them my message!"

This time Jonah did as he was told. He walked into the middle of Ninevah and he shouted out, "God is angry with you! In forty days he will pull your city down!"

The people of Ninevah believed Jonah, and were very sorry they had been so bad. They put on clothes made of old sacks to show God how sorry they were. The king did the same, and he told everyone that they must say their prayers.

"We must all change our ways!"
he ordered. "We must promise God
we will never tell lies or cheat each
other ever again!"

God saw how sorry the king and the
people of Ninevah were. He smiled,
and changed his mind.

"They are good now," he said.
"I will leave their city alone."

But Jonah was very angry with God. "I knew you'd forgive them," he said. "They are my enemies, but you are looking after them." And Jonah marched off to sit at the edge of the city.

God looked at Jonah sitting in the hot sunshine. He smiled to himself, and made a tall leafy plant grow up. Jonah was very happy indeed to be in the shade.

The next morning God made the plant die. Jonah stamped his feet. "Why did you do that?" he demanded.

"Well," God said, "you didn't make the plant grow. You didn't look after it, or water it – but you are still very sorry that it's gone. If you can be sorry about one little plant, don't you think I can be sorry for a whole city?"

"Oh," said Jonah. "Yes. I see now."

For Roan, with love
V.F.

For Bubba, with love
J.C.

First published 2000 by Walker Books Ltd
87 Vauxhall Walk, London SE11 5HJ

This edition published 2009

2 4 6 8 10 9 7 5 3 1

Text © 2000 Vivian French

Illustrations © 2000 Jane Chapman

The right of Vivian French and Jane Chapman to be identified as author
and illustrator respectively of this work has been asserted by them in accordance with
the Copyright, Designs and Patents Act 1988

This book has been typeset in Sassoon Primary

Printed in Singapore

British Library Cataloguing in Publication Data:
a catalogue record for this book is available from the British Library

ISBN 978-1-4063-2312-2
www.walker.co.uk